SNOOPY STARS
— AS —
THE BRANCH MANAGER

Charles M. Schulz

ℛℛ
RAVETTE BOOKS

First published by
Ravette Books Limited 1988

Printed and bound in Great Britain
for Ravette Books Limited,
3 Glenside Estate, Star Road, Partridge Green,
Horsham, Sussex RH13 8RA
by Cox & Wyman Ltd, Reading

ISBN 1 85304 065 7

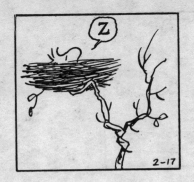

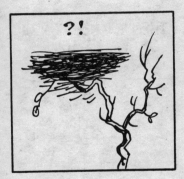

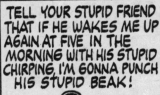

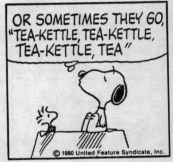

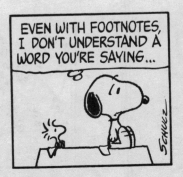

5-29

© 1982 United Feature Syndicate, Inc.

I WON'T SAY THAT WOODSTOCK IS PREJUDICED

9-10

BUT SOMETIMES HIS OPINIONS ARE A LITTLE BIT SLANTED...

3-30

© 1983 United Feature Syndicate, Inc.

4-4

JOE FORKLIFT

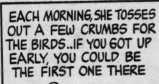

GEE, I DON'T KNOW..
I REALLY THINK YOU'D
BETTER GO WITHOUT
ME..THANKS ANYWAY...

·SIGH·

7-5

© 1984 United Feature Syndicate, Inc.

ACTUALLY, NOTHING
COULD INTEREST ME
LESS THAN GOING TO
A SEED TASTING!

Other Snoopy titles published by Ravette Books

Snoopy Stars in this series

No. 1	Snoopy Stars as The Flying Ace	£1.95
No. 2	Snoopy Stars as The Matchmaker	£1.95
No. 3	Snoopy Stars as The Terror of the Ice	£1.95
No. 4	Snoopy Stars as The Legal Beagle	£1.95
No. 5	Snoopy Stars as The Fearless Leader	£1.95
No. 6	Snoopy Stars as Man's Best Friend	£1.95
No. 7	Snoopy Stars as The Sportsman	£1.95
No. 8	Snoopy Stars as The Scourge of the Fairways	£1.95
No. 10	Snoopy Stars as The World Famous Literary Ace	£1.95
No. 11	Snoopy Stars as The Great Pretender	£1.95
No. 12	Snoopy Stars as The Dog-Dish Gourmet	£1.95

Colour landscapes

First Serve	£2.95
Be Prepared	£2.95
Stay Cool	£2.95
Shall We Dance?	£2.95
Let's Go	£2.95
Come Fly With Me	£2.95

Black and white landscapes

It's a Dog's Life	£2.50
Roundup	£2.50
Freewheelin'	£2.50
Joe Cool	£2.50
Chariots For Hire	£2.50
Dogs Don't Eat Dessert	£2.50
You're on the Wrong Foot Again, Charlie Brown	£2.50

Weekenders

No. 1 Weekender	£4.95

All these books are available at your local bookshop or news-agent, or can be ordered direct from the publisher. Just tick the titles you require and fill in the form below. Prices and availability subject to change without notice.

Ravette Books Limited, 3 Glenside Estate, Star Road, Partridge Green, Horsham, West Sussex RH13 8RA

Please send a cheque or postal order, and allow the following for postage and packing. UK: 45p for one book plus 30p for each additional book.

Name ....

Address ....

....